FREE ONLINE LIFE-COACHING WORKSHOPS

TUESDAY 7PM~8:30PM
LIVE ON ZOOM

ZOOM ID: 5848 455 888
(Passcord: 1111)

SATURDAY 8PM~10PM (PT)
LIVE ON FACEBOOK

https://www.facebook.com/
LoveAndGratitudeStation

THURSDAY 8PM~10PM (PT)
LIVE ON FACEBOOK

https://www.facebook.com/
Sun.Age.Success

Scan QR to get a FREE copy of the book ($25 value)
www.superlifesecretcodes.com (778) 918-8177, (604) 230-1319

SUPER
LIFE
Secret Codes

SAY
NO TO
DEPRESSION

Everything you need to know about
depression and how to beat it

MASTER TED SUN

TABLE OF CONTENTS

TABLE OF CONTENTS

CH 3 ENERGY BALANCE IS THE WAY TO SOLVE ALL PROBLEMS

TABLE OF CONTENTS

CH 4 SAY GOODBYE TO DEPRESSION BY APPLYING THE RIGHT METHODS

TABLE OF CONTENTS

CH 5   WHEN THE MIND, BODY, AND SOUL RESONATE WITH THE UNIVERSE, YOU WILL FIND HAPPINESS IN LIFE

AUTHOR'S FORWARD

SAY NO TO DEPRESSION

In the 21st century, people in science and technology focus on developing products to benefit the well-being of all humans. However, more people have developed depression and bipolar disorder and many illnesses have derived from depression. So far, the development and treatment results for this critical issue are limited, and patients continue to struggle even after seeing top medical doctors. As a result, many people feel helpless and miserable, so many of their families also suffer as they witness treatment after treatment, all failing to cure or improve depression.

Even with money and resources allocated to this illness, there are few effective anti-depression drugs or feasible solutions that have significantly helped patients. I have witnessed too many cases of depression destroying a person's life and I feel obligated to write this book to explain the truth about depression, what it really is, the causes of depression, and solutions for it. This will be the most complete explanation of depression that the world has ever been given.

In 2014, I was giving the *Say No to Depression* lecture at the Richest Life Center in the USA, and I explained and analyzed the problems associated with depression and bipolar disorder. Everyone was surprised to find that the root cause of the problem is an imbalanced energy field. A healthy person should have 100% positive energy, but because of life experiences and other various reasons, his energy field falls below 50%, which then induces depression that causes damage to the mind, body, and soul.

In the *Say No to Depression* book, I will explain step-by-step the causes, structure, changes, and solutions to depression. I also want to point out that Energy plays an important role in one's life. Therefore, I intend to share everything I know, withholding absolutely nothing.

I must be honest that this theory is beyond human knowledge and is based on Universal truths and wisdom, which I have converted into the simplest human narrative to convey the corresponding relationship, structure, and mode of operation of the big Universe and the small Universe. This messaging helps the world change the existing perception of depression and uses simple words to help people understand depression to avoid wasting time, money, and energy on treatments that do not work.

In recent years, around the world, I have met many people suffering from depression or bipolar disorder, but those who followed my methods have recovered successfully. These people are proof that the *Say No to Depression* theories are based on actual case studies, and the results are empirical evidence. I hope someday this set of theories

I have put forward can be spread worldwide, so people no longer suffer from this illness and waste unnecessary time and energy with empty prescriptions that lead to nightmares and regrets. I sincerely hope that the *Say No to Depression* book will be a shining light, guiding the world and giving great help, so depression and related illnesses can be cured.

My other book, *Super Life Secret Codes*, has shared the importance of balancing positive and negative energy and how this affects a person's present life and future. This is crucial to every second in life, and its impact is far beyond your wildest imagination. The book's readers, who have been enlightened, have created a successful blueprint for the future. Unfortunately, many people still do not have an affinity with the book and are still searching. If you can encounter the book, the remedies to the root of all problems. Do not underestimate the simple words used in the book, and I hope you will grasp and cherish the meaning and importance of the book and its effect on your life.

Over the years, with my sincere belief that "The Universe has love and everything exists with love," I have shared the Universal truths in books, songs, lectures, and curriculum. My goal is to help people learn the concepts and methods to have a happy and meaningful life. Only when life is full of hope, happiness, and abundance can people have a clear path to a better future. Therefore, whatever the reason you encountered this book today, I sincerely invite you to learn the *Super Life Secret Codes* system and let us connect to spread positive energy to everyone.

When you realize that many affinities are scarce, cherish this one and apply it in your life, then health, family success, social harmony, and a perfect world will no longer be wishful thinking or a dream. So, through your efforts and sincere practice, you will attain true happiness. I hope all the readers in the world will feel my sincerity and understand the common purpose of all mankind for the future. I also invite you to read my other books and listen to my songs at your leisure. If you are looking for a more advanced program, you can join my lectures and courses. You will be amazed to find that happiness is right in front of you and you can have a life of no regrets and extraordinary achievements.

With sincerity, I believe that we can collectively build a better world for today and the future.

– Master Ted Sun

October 2018, Nevada, USA

CH 1

WHERE DOES DEPRESSION COME FROM?

A field of physical and mental medicine that is not understood

This publication, *Say No to Depression*, aims to share everything about depression and clarify the many unexplained illnesses and their root causes.

The concepts I convey in this book tap into an area of the human body and mind that the current state of medical studies and medicine do not understand.

Discover the password of life, then your future will be bright

Most people hold the concept of "hard work equals success," but the leaks in life quietly surround you and produce symptoms such as cancer, depression, bipolar disorder, and other psychological-related illnesses.

When you enter the *Super Life Secret Codes system*, your hidden depression will be swept away. However, you must play your part to learn and follow all the steps diligently to strive forward in physical life and spiritual life.

Once you absorb and connect with the Universal teachings, you can achieve abundance and happiness; otherwise, anything can be unpredictable in the world.

Always remember, the only thing constant in the Universe is change.

Depression creates negative energy that becomes an illness

Depression means blockage, which creates pressure (a form of energy). Once this energy inside your body accumulates, depression arises. Depression is the beginning of many illnesses.

For example, being late for work causes you to get scolded by your boss and ruins your mood for the whole day. But if there were a surge of positive energy to flush out the depressing energy quickly, your mood could improve immediately. However, if you cannot remove the negative and depressing feeling in your mind within a short time, this feeling will create a chemical reaction and affect you.

When more depressing feelings accumulate and exceed your level of tolerance, then it will create great harm to your mind, body, and soul.

Super Health Secret Codes can relieve symptoms of depression

The methods mentioned in my book *Super Health Secret Codes*, can relieve symptoms of depression. For example, issues with daily bowel movements can affect many aspects of body, mind, and soul.

If some organs function poorly, circulation can be impaired and cause problems with your bowel movements. This discomfort, if prolonged, can lead to the early stage of depression. A simple bowel movement issue is enough to trigger uneasiness and depression.

1.5

There are inherited depression factors in life

When I look further into the life map of certain people, I can see that depression has set in and that they were born with it.

This indicates that the depression factor has pre-existed in someone's fate, putting these people in the **congenital depression** group and at a high risk for cancer.

1.6

Imbalanced energy exacerbates the psychological burden

With the accumulation of many problems and worries in life, one triggering point can cause an imbalance of energy that will exacerbate your psychological burden.

It is very likely that a person can suffer from depression overnight. This sudden consequence is hard to handle and cannot be explained by science and technology.

The loss of energy is the main cause of depression

The energy field of an average person should have positive energy of 100%. Babies are born pure and innocent with lots of positive energy, often shown through their laughter. So much positive energy, that the baby's urine in some cultures is considered a healing power.

As they grow up, they worry about many life matters and encounter obstacles and internal struggles. This leads to endless negative emotions.

Because of daily events, their mood fluctuates, causing a gradual loss of energy. Combine this with having a bad luck year and a weak energy field, and their pressure increases, so energy will drop even more drastically, leading them to feel depressed.

The effect of being depressed is not as simple as it seems

Being depressed is not confined to a particular race or gender and can affect anyone. Therefore, everyone needs to be self-protected.

Postpartum depression is caused by the spiritual bond between the baby and the mother during pregnancy, making both mother and child inseparable. However, when the baby is born out of the womb, the energy field is also brought out, causing a massive loss of maternal energy in the mother. Suddenly the physical and mental situation has changed dramatically. Thus, the mother is depressed.

Some people can get through the gloom of postpartum depression easily. However, some people have a long-lasting inability to improve, or it worsens to a potentially fatal ending. This proves that depression produces a complex and multi-layered problem and is not just a literal meaning.

Depression is self-inflicted

If the heart is not settled, one will feel sad and depressed, and they will drag others down with their depression. Always wish yourself and others well in life. Try to achieve harmony and peace where each person can succeed and have a good life.

Most people with depression do not know they have it. Most of depression is self-inflicted.

If you always try to be difficult and cause pain to others, based on the principle of action and reaction, you will inevitably experience many negative effects. Everything happens for a reason; you are responsible for your actions.

The intrusion of depression is often unexpected

Depression is not distant, it may be near, and it could happen without warning.

Sometimes you look healthy on the outside, but it is possible to have an unexpected factor happen to generate various effects causing your energy field to collapse and disintegrate overnight.

Follow every aspect of "Di Zi Gui*" to ensure that you do not generate any leak of energy in your life.

*Di Zi Gui: Standard for being a good human.

Constantly rationalizing one's behavior is the first sign of obsessive-compulsive disorder

Past and present events will accumulate and eventually get entangled, making them difficult to comprehend. Therefore, the soul is filled with countless complex memories and data from past and present lives.

Sometimes, you do not know the gap between the past and present is too big, and you think that your actions are beneficial and virtuous, so then you constantly rationalize your behavior. This is the first sign of obsessive-compulsive disorder.

On the surface, you think you have solved the problem, but you did not, and you have not bridged the gap between the past and present.

CH 2

CURRENT MAINSTREAM MEDICINE HAS
NO CURE FOR DEPRESSION

To clarify, depression can stem from this life or past lives

The treatments of Western medicine provide a long-term band-aid to those with depression, prolonging the illness. Whether the illness can be improved depends on an individual's energy and merits.

Each person's life lessons are beyond this lifetime. To clarify it, depression can stem from this life or past lives.

To solve depression once and for all, look not only at data from this life, as it is just the tip of the iceberg. The only way to find a solution is to consider this life data and past lives data.

This is an extremely important concept!

A subject that is difficult to understand in mainstream medicine today

The source of blockage is due to unsolved past knots. As for nature, depression is difficult to clearly classify as a single illness type. This is a subject difficult to understand in mainstream medicine today.

Some people have erratic symptoms. Sometimes depressed and sometimes manic-depressive, making the condition more aggravating.

Under a doctor's care, they can only adjust dosage or type of drug.

I suggest all people follow the concepts and directions I explained to study and treat depression. Otherwise, failure will be inevitable.

Taking medication, regardless of the length of time, does not resolve the problems

When the energy level drops below 50%, problems arise. The typical symptom feels wrong and provokes the desire to seek medical attention.

After a diagnosis, the doctor most likely will state a slight depression condition. Then prescribe medication for the patient, so the symptoms will improve.

When patients take medication, they are filled with hope and see small short-term results. But as time goes on, the effects become less and less. Unfortunately, the doctor can only increase the dose or change to a stronger medication to achieve temporary improvement.

How auditory hallucinations and illusions are produced

Medical treatment uses certain chemical compositions to control the central nervous system of a patient. However, this improvement is just a temporary thing.

The chemicals drop the energy level, and when the energy level goes below 25%, the body becomes just a shell.

At this moment, other spirits in the energy field are now stirring and trying to invade the patient's body.

Once in, the spirit(s) will interfere, and the individual will have many hallucinations or illusions.

There are many spirits living in the same body

Nowadays, it is difficult for mainstream medicine to explain and prove there are spirits in the body. So, it is categorized as **hallucinations**.

In fact, what patients with depressive disorders, see and hear while hallucinating, are true and not a figment of imagination or fabricated.

This indicates that a spirit(s) has invaded the body.

To treat this, doctors have no choice but to increase medication dosage or prescribe a stronger medication. The medical industry is helpless in dealing with this phenomenon.

When the energy field drops below 10%, something deeply regrettable can happen.

Many patients take their own lives by self-inflicted wounds, overdose, or hanging.

The severity of depression is closely related to the accumulation of personal merits.

To recover, one needs to accumulate enough merits

Physical and mental derailment is not only in depression. Obsessive-compulsive disorder is also an invisible body and mind-killer.

Cases of OCD patients imposing pressure and stress on partners or children are increasing.

This illness stems from many unfinished grievances from past and present life. Creating cause and effect of negative karma between each other.

OCD is the effect of negative karma, and it is just one scene out of a whole movie. Most people involved with OCD only see what is in front of them and do not realize how they arrived at the point they are at.

From a medical viewpoint, mental illness is difficult to recover from. However, those with enough merits can have milder symptoms and recover. This recovery is because of their merits and not because of the skill of a doctor or the effectiveness of the medicine.

The direction of human evolution must be adjusted immediately

Science and technology in the world are very developed, and this development is beneficial but still cannot determine the origin of all the illnesses in modern civilization. Therefore, this is a huge challenge for all mankind.

The direction of human development must be adjusted immediately; otherwise, even as civilization evolves, there will be little improvement.

Regarding depression, follow the methods I have described, and people can protect themselves from illness and turn pain into joy. There is also no need to look further into medical breakthroughs.

CH 3

ENERGY BALANCE IS THE WAY TO SOLVE ALL PROBLEMS

The relationship between energy and life

Energy balance is how to solve all problems. When you learn the *Super Life Secret Codes* system, you do not want to be selective about the problems nor ignore the personal leaks.

When you encounter problems you can hardly face or want to resist, this is an important moment to choose.

Think about the role that energy plays in life, and the relationship between energy and life. Understand this, and you can solve these unsolvable problems.

Balancing positive and negative energy is the key

A person, who has access to the book *Super Life Secret Codes* must quickly balance positive and negative energy.

If the positive energy continues to leak, this will lead to the invasion of an outer spirit(s).

There have been cases where an average person went insane overnight. This is an example of cause and effect and results from his negligence.

"Di Zu Gui" is a guide to generating a positive mindset and living

Whether depression is solved depends on how many merits you have. If you do not use the concepts of *Super Life Secret Codes* to change yourself, getting rid of depression is difficult.

Many people belong to a high-risk group that potentially can suffer from depression, and there's a good chance that you and I are one of them.

Without merits, once a person suffers from depression, generating the positive energy needed to reverse depression is challenging and complicated.

Everyone should implement the methods of *Super Life Secret Codes* and practice one hundred percent to accumulate merits and elevate their spiritual life.

"Di Zu Gui*" is a guide for people to generate a positive mindset and living. Instantly plugging leaks and removing past bad habits and biases. It is the best tool to prevent the domino effect of negative things. Do an experiment for yourself.

*Di Zi Gui: Standard for being a good human.

Implementing "Di Zụ Gui" to increase positive energy

Implementing "Di Zu Gui" to the whole family is important. Always monitor yourself closely and watch out for leaks at every moment in life.

People who pay attention to everything they do daily will align with the guidelines of "Di Zu Gui."

Implementation of "Di Zu Gui" to the whole family will generate positive energy and harmony to reduce the many unnecessary problems of life.

Awaken the innocence of pure goodness

Regardless of the depression or symptoms, all the results are negative energy. Each symptom has its corresponding source.

Most energy loss comes from past debt, from this life or past lives. Everything can be traced from the life map.

If a person can have access to the *Super Life Secret Codes* book, they can grasp the opportunity to modify and manage energy. Awaken the childlike innocence of pure goodness.

Early prevention of depression or bipolar-related illnesses starts from a small place and stops the gradual expansion of problems.

Positive energy can overpower depression

Recently, the news showed old people in nursing homes fighting and abusing each other.

Those who were abused were healthy and had good lives but eventually died painlessly. On the other hand, those who abused others usually had many sicknesses and suffered throughout their old age and eventually died a slow and painful death.

Everybody's fate and story are different. If they have enough positive energy, they can overpower depression, prevent suffering, and have a smooth-sailing life.

If there is not enough positive energy, the outcome can be detrimental. Therefore, we should not take a chance.

Bask in the Sun

If you have felt the influence of depression a little bit, please ask yourself if you agree with the concepts of *Super Life Secret Codes*? If you still have doubts about the book's contents, it is recommended to read it repeatedly until you understand and agree with the concepts in the book.

Do not give up on *Super Life Secret Codes*, and find that glimmer of hope to solve your problems.

In addition, go outside to bask in the Sun. Enjoy the immense energy that the Sun provides. Breathe in the fresh air and feel the love from the Universe. Do a deep reflection of your narrow and small heart compared to the vastness of the Universe.

Find out the main reason for energy loss

There is a common trait in patients with depression. They are reluctant to admit or face that they have depression.

So, the relatives and friends must assist and encourage the patients to reflect on their past to look for the causes of the continuous positive energy loss or leaks.

Once the causes are found, the patient must communicate and negotiate with the negative energy to find a win-win solution.

Daily practice is how to solve depression completely

When you suffer from depression, it often makes you feel uncomfortable and frustrated. All this is due to the negative energy.

First, you must create as much positive energy as you can. For example, chant "Mighty Sun" and go outside to bask in the Sun's energy. This generates positive energy and can mitigate the effects of negative energy.

Most importantly, practice diligently every day, and this will solve depression once and for all.

Songs with positive energy can elevate a person's energy level

People whose symptoms are too severe to do anything and cannot practice visualization meditation can listen to the song "Because of the Sun" written by Master Ted Sun.

Start by listening to the song to change your energy level, then recite the Four Phrase Gratitude Mantra*, eventually, your positive energy will arise.

And then listen to Master Ted Sun's other songs and elevate your energy level to where you can slowly practice the visualization meditations (refer to *Super Life Secret Codes*).

*Gratitude to the Universe, gratitude to the future. Gratitude to the Universe, gratitude to love. Gratitude to the Universe, gratitude to love. Gratitude to the Universe, gratitude to all answers accounted for.

Making progress every day

Only the Universe, the Mighty Sun, and the patient can save himself when the illness is too severe.

Everything revolves around the basis of energy. Whether you can **mobilize energy** is a critical factor.

Making progress every day, is the driving force for continuous positive development to naturally cure your illness.

You do not have to believe what I am saying, just experiment

When you comply with the techniques, also study "Di Zu Gui" and integrate them into your life, so there will be a tremendous improvement in your physical and mental health. You do not have to believe what I am saying. Just experiment. See the results and then believe it.

When you diligently practice, honor the teachings, and be grateful to the source, you can protect yourself from depression. In addition, if your energy level drops, you will have ways to correct it.

When you are prepared and have practiced diligently, any possibility of depression or a low energy level can instantly be avoided. And with this new mindset, you can improve your life.

A false understanding leads to complex interactions between the mind and soul

The process of depression is when your energy field is under the influence of yourself or other spiritual anomalies that produce irregular behaviors in you.

For example, patients with OCD have extreme behavior of excessive restlessness and anxiety. This is caused by an imbalance in their energy field.

While they are acting out of this energy imbalance, they think their actions are normal but cannot explain why they do what they do.

A false understanding leads to complex interactions between the mind and soul.

Don't be attached to past habits

Even seeing famous doctors will not benefit you much if you have insufficient merits. Ultimately, you are just an actor that plays the story created by your past lives in your life.

When you experience negative things in your daily life, you cannot be attached to your old habits, and you must make changes and diligently practice the methods in *Super Life Secret Codes*.

Find the root of the problem and eliminate all sources that can cause negative energy. This will solve many problems in your life.

"Save for a rainy day"

When your energy is low, any little thing is enough to make you miserable.

Just like when you have a toothache, any little touch or bump can be painful.

Let me emphasize to "save for a rainy day." Build up as much positive energy as possible while you can. There are many cases of people nearing death that experience extreme sadness over not having the energy to perform the most basic and routine daily things.

Now that you know this concept of "save for a rainy day," do it now, before it is too late, and the problems become irreversible regrets or require 10 times more energy to solve.

Suddenly becoming sensitive is a sign of insufficient energy

People with depression have a low energy level, and when they encounter situations, they react erratically, and this causes the illness to worsen.

People with little merits and low energy are more likely to suffer problems that affect the body, mind, and soul. Examples of this are obsessive-compulsive disorder, manic-depressive disorder, depression, etc.

When you feel like you are suddenly becoming sensitive, it is a sign of insufficient energy.

People with psychic ability and can see spirits and read into the future need to be very careful because they were born with an energy deficiency.

Ability and wisdom for enlightenment

Whether things are easy or not, treat every day matters as practice. Practice one by one until you master them all.

Through practice, you will see growth and physical improvement, which naturally will give you confidence to welcome abundance into your life.

With enough positive energy, problems that are difficult to overcome in your past life are now easy to resolve.

Exercising your ability and wisdom for dealing with life, helps you see through any problem. Like an upper grader looking at the lower grade level material, what was tedious and complicated before, is now very easy. This can be achieved only through diligent practice.

Self-reliance is the only way to overcome depression

When life is hopeless, things are miserable, and you feel extremely depressed, focus on being more self-reliant. This is the only way to overcome depression. Never depend on sympathy and care from others.

Being balanced between mind and body helps attract continuous positive energy, so you can work on your soul.

If you lose hope, your energy will be drained, and your heart will be empty. Even help from family and friends will be useless.

Building a positive atmosphere prevents depression

The study of mankind, to a high level, can be called Science or Philosophy, and Spirituality.

Spirituality is to monitor how we manage our body, mind, and soul, every day.

Life experiences, good and bad, help train the mind to gradually find peace and harmony instead of chaos.

Building a positive atmosphere prevents depression. Start by building a good foundation to prevent future problems.

Control is in your hands

Some psychics have a special connection with the spiritual world, and they feel privileged.

However, psychics are born with an energy deficiency, making them sensitive to their surroundings while others feel fine.

Increasing your energy is the key. You need not rely on other spirits to tell you how to play your role; instead, you can be self-reliant and succeed in life.

Positive energy is the best natural barrier

Prevention is better than treatment. Positive energy is the best natural barrier. Follow the laws of the Universe and resonate with the Universe, and you can receive blessings from the Universe.

If depression continues to intensify, the pain will increase, and you will suffer tremendously.

First, you must find sunlight. Then, gradually increase the sunlight in the room. However, do not add too much light too quickly. If this happens, the spirit cannot adapt, and this exercise will backfire.

When your heart is wide open, there is no pressure

Depression can last from years to decades. When the stress pushes you over the edge, the effect can be devastating.

The Analects of Confucius states, "The past is irreparable, but there is still time to make changes for the future." So from now on, watch out for signs of low energy and depression.

With the many things going on in life, if you are consumed by pain and negative energy, it is difficult to do well in life.

Pressure intensifies as it reaches maximum capacity within a certain space. Imagine your heart is wide open, then is the pressure you feel as strong as you think it is?

With the blessings of the Universe, depression goes away

Merit building requires daily accumulation, so do not wait until the last minute to begin. You must continuously build. There is no time for a pause or break. This is how you can solve your problems permanently.

Everything in life comes from energy. The results of your life are the report card of how much merits you have accumulated.

Many problems in life seem unsolvable, but finding a solution is a breeze with the *Super Life Secret Codes* system. When you have blessings from the Universe, depression goes away.

Life is like a play, and often times, the plot is not what you want

Everyday life is like a play. To have an amazing play can be difficult because the positive and negative energy from our past lives make things hard to control.

Think about whether you have had the following experience. Often, you want to have an amazing play; however, you are haunted by past family and life challenges that lead to many other things going wrong.

You have no way out, and you are facing enormous pressure in life. Are you committed to finding the solution? You are already on the path to solving your problems. Be brave and strive forward.

CH 4

SAY GOODBYE TO DEPRESSION BY APPLYING THE RIGHT METHODS

Secret weapons to overcome depression or manic-depressive disorder

Super Life Secret Codes system is essential for fighting depression. The concepts in the book are antidotes to overcoming depression or manic-depressive disorder.

There are countless switches in the body, and if the negative switch is accidentally turned on, a lot of trouble comes along with it.

The solution depends on the adequacy of energy and merits. This is the biggest problem-solving factor.

I would rather be owed than owe others

There is a saying, "The wolf has a winning game, when the shepherds quarrel." If you take advantage of others to get what you want, be certain that someone is nearby looking to take advantage of you. In the end, there is no real winner.

One case is the owner of a well-known casino, and at 50, he was making a lot of money but was suffering from depression. It was very severe, so he had to leave his job to seek medical attention.

His condition was the effect of his casino, which caused many gamblers to lose money. Sometimes, people went bankrupt, and some even lost their businesses and families or committed suicide.

The lessons here are that we should be honest and virtuous. Do not be arrogant or complacent. Follow the "I would rather be owed than owe others" ideology. If you do take advantage of others, karma will serve you, and the consequences are unimaginable.

Let go of grudges to save yourself

Some people live in their past, remembering and holding on to painful experiences. They relive the pain every day and cannot let go.

Now you come across the book *Super Life Secret Codes*. If you follow the methods, you can bid farewell to your painful past. Adopt the concept in the book and implement "Di Zu Gui" into your daily life. Don't wait. Just do it.

Reflect on your grudges, like past regrets, hatred, and unforgivable people. Then let them go, to save yourself.

Holding on to past beliefs, aggravates depression

Recognize that if you do not try to solve depression right now, and you adhere to past beliefs, your symptoms will worsen.

Your life will not improve, and you will end your life with regret, sadness, and hatred.

Please think deeply. Is this the life you want to live and the ending you imagined?

Manifest first and then practice being grateful for everything

Whether depression can be solved or not is determined by your mind. Whether you can open your mind is related to your present and past lives.

It does not matter if you can switch your mindset to positive. The one thing you should do now is to practice gratitude for everything.

Manifest first, then change will occur. If you do not change, energy will not shift and ultimately, you will be stuck.

4.6

There is a solution to everything in life

When a person is sick, relatives and friends express care and concern and are enthusiastic about giving many opinions and suggestions for treatment.

This sometimes deviates the patient from the tools of *Super Life Secret Codes*, which will delay the golden opportunities for healing.

There is a solution to everything in life. Whether you find the solution depends on if you utilize the right tools.

Regardless of the reason, if you find your energy level dropping, pause, take a deep breath and visualize the Sun and listen to Master Ted Sun's healing music.

Chant "Mighty Sun"

When the situation is urgent, chant "Mighty Sun."

Why is the name "Mighty Sun" important? Because we are surrounded by data and power, the Sun is the key to accessing it.

The name "Mighty Sun" is a signal to the Universe, and if you are a virtuous person, when you chant this, you will be granted energy.

This signal can pause the execution of negative energy and provide some time for your situation.

Don't overindulge and miss the golden opportunity of healing

Patients in the initial stages of depression often think of everything with certainty and feel good about themselves. However, as time goes on, they gradually lose the ability to fight depression.

Once the critical point is passed, even the best doctor, treatment, and medication cannot help.

Overindulgence and their failure to solve their problems cause them to miss the golden opportunity for healing.

Don't treat people with negative thoughts

By observing the signs of climate change, one could estimate the future weather in the past. Unfortunately, today's storms do not follow the norm and cannot be predicted.

For example, hurricanes, unusual tornadoes, or other natural disasters are often difficult to predict or prevent.

Therefore, to avoid depression, we must not have negative thoughts about people. Please remember, that every thought has a corresponding point. The Earth is round. What goes around comes around.

Positive energy is mutually beneficial

When replenishing our positive energy, if the process is interfered with by negative energy, the head-to-head battle will lead to a lose-lose situation because you are against a collaborative effort of negative energy.

Use the methods of *Super Life Secret Codes*, to leverage merits with your negative energy. This will increase your ability to negotiate with your negative energy to achieve a mutual benefit. This is what the *Super Life Secret Codes* system is all about.

Have trust in the Universe

People should have the mindset of "realize, then let go of things and have trust in the Universe." From this, people should reflect on whether being opinionated and rigid has made life better.

Based on many people's lives, time does not resolve issues when one holds on to his opinions.

We must have trade-offs between the body and mindset. Do not let ignorance and negligence continue to accumulate mistakes and then turn them into complicated and unrepairable problems.

Forgive others to free yourself

Please carefully think again about the pain and anger you have. Is it as serious as you feel or imagine? Is it worth your while to hold on to your opinions and be unwilling to forgive others, thus trapping yourself in pain and agony?

If you think you have the right understanding and logic and believe that no one in the world can influence your choices, you must be accountable for all consequences.

Decisions have consequences. Do you want to have endless pain and troubles? Or do you bring in love and gratitude and then be healthy, happy, and free?

Prepare yourself for the unknown

Consider the possibilities of "what if" and remember that being opinionated, and rigid does not benefit yourself or others.

Change yourself now and let go of your ego to avoid being irrational, which will cause irreversible issues in the future.

You do not know whether tomorrow arrives first or the unpredictable factors, so seize your time and diligently consider the possibilities of "what if," to prepare yourself for the unknown.

Balance your mind and enjoy life lessons

Life experiences create our life lessons. Learn to balance your mind and enjoy and learn from life lessons so they do not become our distractions.

Cherish the opportunities and build upon them to enhance your spiritual life.

Pain will pass

As you continue to practice and your wisdom grows, you will gain more experiences. Gradually you have more clarity and achieve full control of your life.

As you look back at all your pains, worries, and long-term problems, they will no longer be there; they will have passed.

As you reflect on your handling of past problems, you will laugh at how foolish you were.

With the right approach, you will repel emotional disorders

If you use the right methods in the life journey, the most difficult things can be resolved!

Use the *Super Life Secret Codes* system to overcome challenges in life, and gain more confidence.

Trust the Universe so every day of life is stable and solid. Then you will repel emotional disorders.

Completely eliminate depression

Worrying is because many things in your life cause uncertainty, and there is no solution.

Worrying eventually becomes the loss of energy, and when you worry about many things, depression will be with you all the time.

Within a manageable timeframe, tell yourself there is a solution to everything. Through daily practice you will see clearly the root of your problems.

Simplify complex and tedious things, and then you can eliminate depression.

Compliance with the methods to avoid mistakes

Being self-righteous and outspoken, no filter is not the correct attitude that a person should have. Unfortunately, many of those who are cocky and boastful are destitute. This unreasonable attitude alone will anger others, both people and spirits, and leads to a myriad of subsequent problems.

The concept and attitude of cultivation must be treated prudently, and all practices must comply with the methods to avoid mistakes.

Otherwise, the impatient negative energy or spirits cannot see a way out and give up the chance of reincarnation to seek revenge now, causing the individual, who owes, tremendous pain and suffering.

A calm mind generates wisdom to see life clearly

"Compliance with the methods" is not a slogan. It affects you in every aspect of success or failure.

With murky water, it takes a lot of energy to see and catch fish.

The wisemen have often said, "A calm mind generates wisdom to see life clearly." The wisdom here means the overall wisdom that encompasses everything.

When your mind is pure and simple, you will see through life's complications. Your sadness will become happiness and lead you to a worry-free life. This is a state of mind and the manifestation of wisdom.

Reposition life into positive thinking

One's positioning is often derived from the upbringing from a young age.

These ideas that parents have instilled in them may not be correct. These errors will cause problems later in life.

People must follow the truth of the Universe. So, we must re-position life into positive thinking.

Follow "Di Zu Gui," the guideline for being a good human. Then you can solve your problems simply and completely and live a happy life.

Troubles and worries are melting away

People wish to melt away all the pain and worries to welcome abundance in life. Many people's common problems are marital disharmony.

Use the *Super Life Secret Codes* methods to fix the bad habits accumulated for a long time.

If you learn how to appreciate each other, your relationship will naturally be more intimate and harmonious.

Avoid the causes of depression

You may not notice this but saying negative things irritates the people around you. Constant negative comments and getting things off your chest will produce negative energy and eventually return to hurt you like poison.

Therefore, do not indulge in speaking recklessly and ruthlessly, which are damaging and cause negative energy, and will lead to depression.

Eliminate negative things and habits as soon as possible

To attain the goal of becoming a Sage, which is the highest quality of a person, you and I must eliminate negative things and habits as soon as possible.

If we follow the laws of the Universe, exactly, then we can enter the new era.

Once our positioning is set to achieve our goal, we must execute. Then things will gradually improve.

This is the way of the Universe, and it is not up to us. If we do not agree and want to do otherwise, this will cause problems for mankind.

4.24

The goal of becoming a Sage

In every moment in life, even a split second of not thinking, can cause a bad decision that will create unwanted outcomes.

To achieve the goal of becoming a Sage, you must set the proper positioning and encourage yourself to execute.

Being a Sage is no longer just a wish. It is now a goal, and you must implement it every day into all aspects of your life.

Achieving the goal described above is not a difficult task, and you must do it so everything in life will gradually improve, from bad to good or good to even better.

4.25

Thinking about how to break through in the existing conditions

Essential Steps 1-2-3 is a daily practice. The more you refine your practice, the better the results. Soon the things you wish for in life will just happen naturally.

An appropriate mechanism should be developed to self-reflect and find a solution. For example, your boss gives you a new project, and the workload is much more than you can handle, so you work like a dog and do a lot of overtime. Sooner or later, your body will get overwhelmed.

After work, you must put yourself in a comfortable state. Thinking about how to breakthrough in the existing conditions will improve yourself and greatly improve work efficiency. This is a wise move.

This method can effectively resolve your life crisis

If you have a severe depression condition, bask in the Sun, visualize the Sun in the sky, and visualize another Sun right in front of you. Then, take deep breaths slowly to receive the nutrients you are lacking.

This method can effectively resolve your life crisis. Do not just believe me. Try it for yourself. Please experiment to obtain your verification to gain confidence. Find no excuses to be depressed.

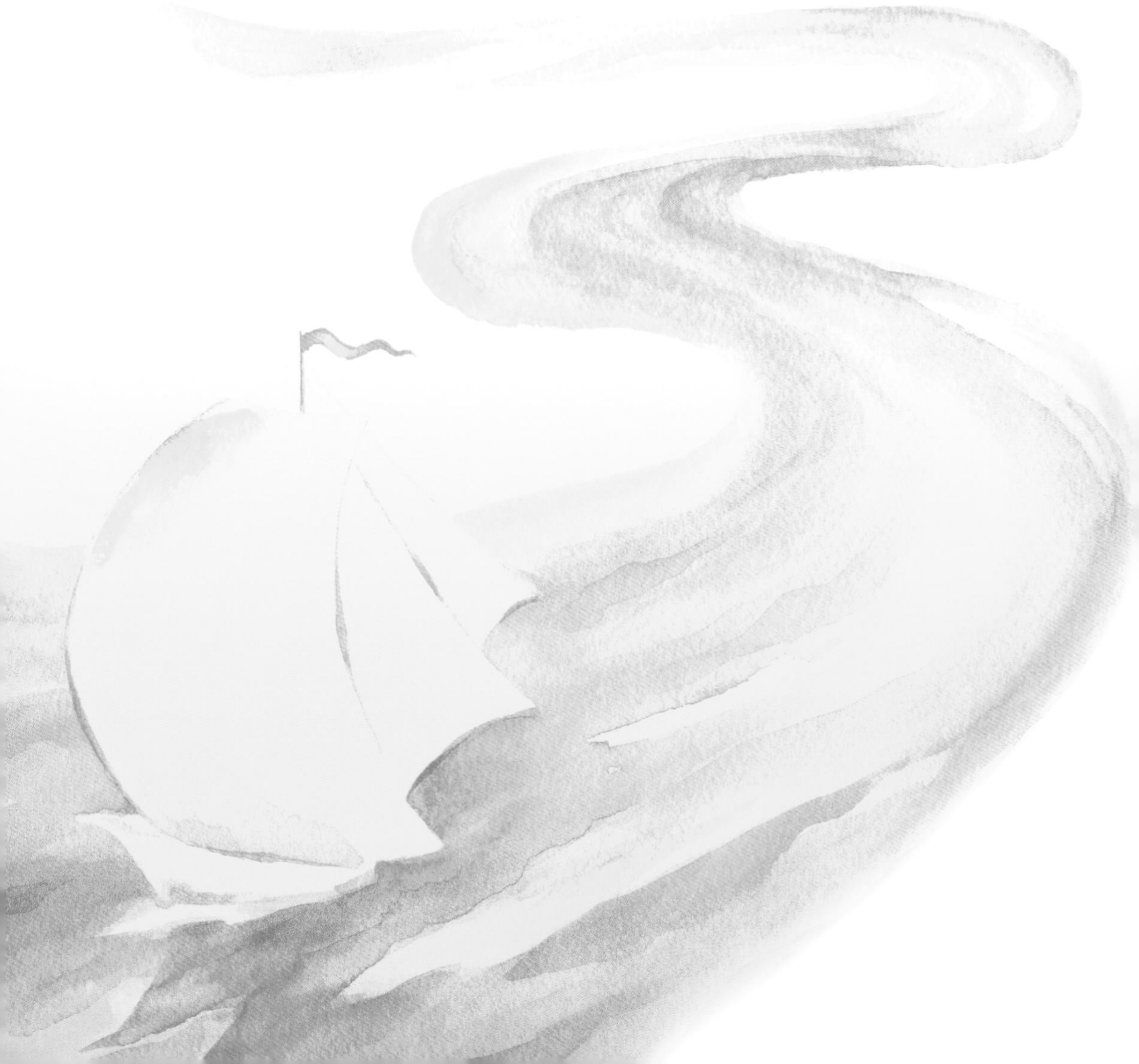

If everything will get better, why do you worry?

Think about this. If everything will get better, why do you worry?

Even patients with severe depression who have suffered pain and disturbances from negative energy (spirits), with the wisdom and correct mindset, can generate merits to pay back the negative energy to stop the pain and disturbances.

So please recognize this. If you follow my methods quickly, you can save time. With high diligence, you shall have more positive results and before you know it, good things will naturally happen to you.

CH 5

WHEN THE MIND, BODY AND SOUL
RESONATE WITH THE UNIVERSE, YOU
WILL FIND HAPPINESS IN LIFE

Delete the bad habits, of past lives and present, from your soul memory

Depression is caused by insufficient energy, making you sensitive to everything. When you follow the *Super Life Secret Codes* system, you will monitor yourself every moment, like a GPS. You will even have the ability to heal yourself.

Often, when you feel a symptom in your body, you get an examination and the results are very shocking. After the diagnosis, the doctor may prescribe some lengthy treatment.

There are so many causes of illness, but most importantly, you need to self-reflect to find the bad habits that caused the leaks. Then plug the leaks and delete the bad habits, from past lives and present, from your soul memory.

Fully understand how to deal with all situations

Some spirits are very active and dynamic. You must be calm to use your wisdom to deal with them.

Your mind must be clear and sharp to find a strategy to deal with the spirits. In addition, you must protect yourself and your family and avoid unnecessary problems.

With diligent practice, your skills will improve, and your sensitivity will increase, giving you more insight and understanding of big and small things in life. You will then be better prepared to deal with all situations.

When your logic is correct, your life path will be clear

When one first learns he has depression, he is overwhelmed and hard to accept.

Imagine your thoughts and logic are energy in pipes. If you have the wrong thoughts or logic, your energy flow will be misguided.

When the energy flow is misguided, it can become blocked and create more complications.

If you do not solve it, your future is bound to suffer. You may experience illnesses like depression or bipolar disorder. Therefore, only when your logic is correct will your life path be clear.

Now is just a little dot on your life timeline

Most people have difficulty letting go of problems they have had for a long time.

Carefully review your past. Look at the events that were so painful and blocked your progress. Holding on to these will affect your mood and cause it to fluctuate.

Life goes on, and every event, good or bad, is just a dot on your life timeline.

Like a little drop of black ink in a bucket of clean water, it pollutes everything. A small grudge in your life can pollute your body, mind, and soul.

Remember to look at your entire spiritual life and realize **now** is just a little dot on your life timeline.

A glimpse of death can be the cure for greed

For people consumed by greed that will not let up, I often advise them to visualize death or watch a video of a body getting cremated.

For the ordinary, a glimpse of death can be a cure for greed by letting the mind calm down and clear through the noise and distractions.

Instead of leaving this life with regrets and unfinished business, why not grab on to your time and transform the map of life to be better now and for the future.

Friction is often caused by overly sensitive positioning

Because your past life positioning is incorrect, you produce many problems.

For example, someone insults you, which makes you angry or some people are rude and that frustrates you.

Friction is often caused by overly sensitive positioning, which creates an imbalance in your mind.

Be careful, as this chain reaction will eventually evolve into a devastating situation.

Reprogram the wrongful mindset and experiences

Based on the law of the immortal soul, the timeline continues to evolve, and your data stays with you.

Most importantly, you must reprogram the wrongful mindset and experiences from your soul memory, correct the improper logic and views, and make sure that the positioning is set in a positive direction. Once on track, good things will come, one after another.

The golden rule is to follow the laws of the Universe

The body works in profound ways.

Like when we eat food, our body automatically transforms the food into nutrients, and then the nutrients become energy for the body.

Wisemen have said, "The wisdom of the Universe is so vast that there is nothing outside, and at the same time, so small there is nothing inside."

Something that seems so small and insignificant for an ordinary person is full of wisdom in the world of the Universal mechanism.

So, the golden rule is to follow the laws of the Universe.

Practice *Super Life Secret Codes* visualization meditations to achieve a sense of comfort

Human beings struggle with understanding things that are not visible through a microscope.

Cells can be subdivided into various structures, and these smaller units can combine and correspond with each other.

If you want every part of your mind and body to receive the correct and positive data, you must apply the right method to program the feeling of **comfort**. Then this feeling will be embedded into your mind and soul.

Practice *Super Life Secrets Codes* visualization meditations to achieve a sense of comfort. This can prevent the possibility of depression and manic depression.

With a real sense of comfort, depression does not exist

Once you have created a feeling of comfort, it is recorded in the soul memory. Then, when you need comfort, it can be easily mobilized.

Once you have the true feeling of abundant comfort, depression does not exist.

From this moment on, work hard in the right direction until you attain perfection and completion in your life.

The type of data stored determines a positive or negative result

When the soul memory stores positive conclusions from many of your life experiences, remember to grab hold of these feelings and embed them into your mind and soul.

For example, when tired but unable to rest on a comfortable bed, resting on a chair can still comfort you and make you happy. Hold on to this satisfying sense of well-being.

When the same situation is happening, your soul memory will retrieve the same conclusions. Therefore, the data stored will determine a positive or negative result.

5.12

It is imperative to reach a win-win situation

Remember that life is filled with many false situations or illusions. Often people unknowingly get sucked into them, which can lead to unbearable illnesses. Be extra careful in every aspect of the process.

Comply to the methods and develop wisdom to deal with all situations in life. It is an imperative and important lesson to reach a win-win situation. Otherwise, every day, the body, mind, and soul will not achieve a balance.

The result is a constant loss of energy, creating a vicious cycle for the future.

The Universe will give you the wisdom to solve your problems

As you continuously practice, when your skills develop to a certain level, the Universe will give you the wisdom to solve your problems.

When you realize the importance of practicing various lessons such as mind switching, meditation, and improving your energy field, you will see that these subjects are interlinked, mutually supportive, and necessary.

You must be self-reliant and improve yourself, then, you can help others join to improve the world.

When you are fully prepared, the Universe will resonate with you

Prepare ahead of time, and when the test comes, you will be calm and confident.

Before the test and challenges in life happen, you should study the material thoroughly and learn from other people's experiences. Grasp the characteristics of the different questions and then learn the keys to solve them.

If you're fully prepared, you will resonate with the Universe. The Universe will help you score exceptionally well on your test.

Problem-solving mastery and proficiency are closely related to depression. Whatever your choice is, it will lead to positive or negative results. Ultimately, you are accountable for everything.

If you do not help yourself, the Universe will not help you

When you diligently comply with the system, you can integrate all the subjects well and eventually attain Sagehood. All aspects of your life will be complete and perfect, so naturally, you can say no to depression.

If you help yourself, the Universe will help you too, but if you do not help yourself, the Universe will not help you.

Life is like a test, and one should always practice for the test by simulating life situations. Embed this simulation into your heart and soul.

Remember the concept of "save for a rainy day" and master as many life situations as possible now to help you achieve success with ease.

Your spiritual life will immediately take off when you have set your mind and mastered all life situations.

Replace no with yes

When you are aware of your thoughts, you must replace no with yes. This will help you get rid of depression much faster.

This viewpoint that comes from your mind, body, and soul creates strength in your heart to focus.

You must believe everything has a solution. If you do, everything in your mind can create reality, and you will experience the concept of one plus one is greater than two.

Remove the impurities interfering with the mind

If you neglect the negative emotions and pressures for a long time, you become trapped in a negative state of mind. This will greatly increase the burden and difficulty of treating your illness.

You must cut the roots of the negative emotions and pressures and fight hard to prevent the problems from reoccurring.

Practice the Essential Steps 1-2-3* every day and do the Repentance and Pledge Making technique with your utmost sincerity. Remove the impurities interfering with your mind, which will prevent the unpredictable problems of the future.

*Essential Steps 1-2-3 is the life transformation and energy management methods in the *Super Life Secret Codes* book.

A chance to rewrite your fate

At the beginning of cleansing, all the burdens and baggage in your life are overwhelming, difficult to sort through, and hard to cleanse in a short while.

If you diligently clean up every day, your heart will become clear and spotless, and things will get easier.

In your soul memory many incomplete memories correspond to the subsequent negative things. With your daily cleaning, you can rewrite your fate.

5.19

A method that holds the ultimate decision-making power

The value of the *Super Life Secret Codes* system is to help you choose between right and wrong. Therefore, cherishing the methods can help you say goodbye to the illnesses of modern society.

The most important thing in the *Super Life Secret Codes* system is the Repentance and Pledge Making technique which holds the ultimate decision-making power.

You can negotiate with your negative energy to reach a compromise with sincerity.

Once a compromise is made, many things can be resolved, and past life debts can be taken care of. Then miracles in life naturally happen.

5.20

Creating a positive atmosphere to increase confidence

It is imperative to practice creating success in all topics of life.

Prove that all your actions are correct and follow the laws of the Universe. Your wisdom will increase in relation to how well you practice and realize.

You must be persistent in creating a positive atmosphere to build up confidence. Monitor yourself in every moment like a GPS to control life's direction.

Turn a crisis into an advantage

A crisis can be an advantage if you turn it into a life lesson to enrich your life. If you do not, the crisis will become negative energy and hold you back in life.

Opportunity is reserved for those who are ready. To improve, you must act and not just talk about it.

Gauge all life situations, be flexible and open-minded, so you can attain the success of completion.

Help people avoid pain and find happiness

The cause of disease and illness today is not just the problem of present life but is closely linked to the debt of your past lives.

If you pay back your debt and follow the laws of the Universe, the Universe will give you love and blessings. When the abundant energy from the Universe activates on you, the negative energy of depression becomes insignificant.

If you are cured of depression and bipolar disorder, consider this being reborn. Please remember to give this world your love and share it with more people to help them avoid pain and find happiness.

Never take it lightly

Say no to depression, and do not let it creep into your life.

Proactively eliminate any possibility of pain and suffering in life and only keep the happy and positive things. Experience all the goodness of the world.

Say no to depression and embed all of the concepts taught in this book deep in your heart.

Everything in life will leave a trace and consequence, so never take it lightly!

There is no reason for you not to succeed

If you follow the methods of *Super Life Secret Codes*, depression and manic-depressive problems will gradually go away and will be replaced with great rewards in your life.

If you do not come to a consensus with negative energy, even the most advanced medication will be useless.

In life, the only way to feel grounded and stable is through self-reliance, which will also speed improvement.

There are many channels and resources for learning in the *Super Life Secret Codes* system.

There's absolutely no reason for you not to succeed! Bless you, my dear friend.

ABOUT

RICHEST LIFE

Richest Life, established in 2011, is an international personal and professional growth and wellness training center. Richest Life has quickly spread globally, helping hundreds of thousands of people take control of life by using the *Super Life Secret Codes* system. Through this system, people increase their positive energy and self-confidence, helping them find happiness and get on a path towards success and abundance. Richest Life provides people of all ages with many mental and physical improvement programs like stress relief, better relationships, health, wealth, and overall energy management.

ABOUT

MASTER TED SUN

Master Ted Sun is a world-renowned speaker and educator, a top-selling author in energy management, Nobel Peace Prize Nominee who passionately studied and experimented with the formulas of life, which led to his breakthrough of discovering the **secret codes** to a super life. He felt an obligation and responsibility to share these codes with everyone with this gift.

In 2010, he wrote his 1st book, *Super Life Secret Codes*, a life manual. Master Ted Sun reveals the secret codes to peace and happiness in the book. By managing and building our energy, we can balance our emotions, life, family, and society. Energy is the key element of life and determines the positive and negative outcomes of all things.

Since 2010, Master Ted Sun has written over 30 books and given tens of thousands of consultations and has seen all types of human predicaments and miseries, and he has concluded that people need proper training to have a balanced and happy life. Master Ted Sun created the *Super Life Secret Codes* system and has given lectures and helped people worldwide regain health, success, and happiness.

SAY NO TO DEPRESSION

Published by Richest Life USA, under the rights granted by
Greenland Success Co Ltd., Taiwan Branch
www.saynotodepressionnow.com

ISBN : 978-0-57-893884-4
Printed in Taiwan.
Second Edition, April 2022
Price: USD 25, CAD 32